REGRETLAND

To THE "Joe" IN ALL
of US.
No Regrets,
Adrienne Holiday

The Rose and the Pickle

A story for all ages, offering an affecting
concept that beauty is unique and, therefore,
impossible to be judged.

The Almighty Dollar Bill

An extraordinary and brilliant story with
the theme that money becomes "Almighty"
when spent in love to create miracles!

The Science of Gifting

A guidebook for removing mental blocks to
receiving love, health and money . . .

Regretland

A Journey to Freedom

A. Golday

WESTLAKE VILLAGE, CALIFORNIA

2008

Published by Regretland Books
1014 S. Westlake Blvd., Suite 14-195
Westlake Village, California 91361

Editor: Aurora LeMere
Illustrator: Elizabeth Berg
Typist: Terri Nigro, Paragon Word Processing
Designer: Jennifer Corr, The Stinehour Press

ISBN 978-0-615-18746-4

First Edition, First Printing—March 2008

Printed by The Stinehour Press in Lunenburg, Vermont U.S.A.
Bound by Roswell Bookbinding in Phoenix, Arizona U.S.A.

To all of the masterful writers who united with me in consciousness in the writing of this book, and to every "Joe" on this planet . . . with the awareness that our destiny will one day be fulfilled when we all reach supreme love and live in the Land of Deity forever.

CONTENTS

Do you have regrets that haunt you, keeping you awake 'til all hours of the night? Do you regret missed opportunities? Are there roads you might have traveled and places you wish you had seen? Have you lost your self-esteem and childhood passions, as disappointments washed them away? Has your need for security prevented you from taking chances that you wish you had taken? Have you withheld your love, keeping it buried in your heart, rather than giving it freely to another? So many people you wanted to love, while some you held onto for too long? Could you have earned more money, invested more wisely, saved for a day like today? Is your bank account depleted as you look back upon the steps not taken to grow wealth? Is this the stormy day you wish you had saved for, as you count your pennies for your daily bread?

Enter a timeless journey where you will explore levels of consciousness that reveal the mental traps that have kept us victims of our past . . . often shackled with heavy chains of despair.

Unlock the key to higher levels of awareness that allow us to create joy and bliss, as we travel with Joe, uncovering our true destiny! Discover a "better way of living . . . ," a new way of viewing your world that brings the rewards of peace of mind and riches beyond your wildest dreams!

Reader, discover the "Joe" that lives in you, and together we will leave Regretland forever and experience bliss.

Pinnacle Mountain

CHAPTER I

Joe is an ordinary kind of guy. His friends look up to him and seek his advice. Perhaps it is his positive attitude and grand smile that endear people to Joe. Every year he travels to the beautiful mountains of Sedona, Arizona, where masterful teachers gather to explore the latest advances in higher consciousness. These renowned philosophers, scientists and religious leaders from the entire globe meet to share their knowledge with the impatient seekers of wisdom, who are searching for that one concept, idea, new philosophy or creative belief that will hold the power to change their lives and bring them happiness and enlightenment.

The orange-colored rock formations created a picturesque setting as these leaders prepared their talks for this year's Pinnacle Mountain Retreat.

Joe was anxious to renew his sense of purpose. Each year upon returning to his life as a baker, he always felt motivated and inspired to write his short self-help column in the local newspaper. His eager friends awaited his return, hoping that Joe's enthusiasm would change their own mundane lives. They enjoyed Joe's bright smile that lit up rooms and seemed to lift the energy of all in his presence. His robust body and warm laughter always brightened the darkest day. Joe enjoyed his food and shared his fine cooking talents with friends in his gourmet kitchen. He earned his living as a baker and most enjoyed the aroma of freshly baked breads. With his white chef's hat set upon his head, he would taste every recipe, asking for suggestions, while trying to keep the crumbs off his beard. His blue-green eyes sparkled with a gleam and his magnanimous nature attracted crowds. If you made his acquaintance, you'd most likely think you had met the most generous person in the world.

Joe had not missed a retreat for fifteen years. As he sorted his clothing in his tiny bungalow, bare of televisions, phones, faxes and computers, he felt a sad feeling of discouragement. He walked to the cafeteria to join the other students where they studied the schedule of events. As excited as he was to be there, somehow this year, unlike earlier times, his life energy seemed to have slowed down and tears often filled his eyes each morning upon awakening. Now middle-aged, Joe was feeling that his life had passed him by. He prided himself on "standing guard" at the gate of his mind to guard his thoughts, as he had learned from many masterful teachers. He was an avid reader of self-help books and life studies. He knew better than to allow himself to feel discouraged or to allow negative thoughts of aging. Yet, with all his conditioned positive thinking, he began to fight with his own thoughts, trying to allow only the good ones to permeate his mind. That defeating voice that often haunted him said, "Why even bother?" The more he resisted, thoughts of an aging body crept into his head as he looked in the mirror, confirming old age, as he viewed the creases in his neck and deep lines along his brow, and the huge circumference of his waist. "I'm running out of time," thought Joe as he looked back over his life. "The best is all behind me now." Joe's energy reflected his thoughts, and his emotions were sinking lower every day. His life certainly wasn't a "walk in the park."

At the opening ceremony that evening the Masters and students sat around the fireside and formed a large circle called the Circle of Truth. Since this is where students had the opportunity to share ideas, Joe talked about a new technique he had developed to assist people to accept greater abundance in their lives and to remove blocks in their thought patterns. In such prestigious company, a feeling of pride filled Joe to have something valuable to share.

Later that night, Joe looked up at the star-filled sky and wondered what special lesson he still needed to discover that might reveal a better way to live. Was the peace of mind and bliss that he sought all these years not really a possibility? His life seemed to pass so quickly while he was busy trying to figure it out. His spirit that once soared was now longing for repair. He settled into his bed, but his restless thoughts wouldn't allow him to sleep. Joe got up and went for a walk around Pinnacle Mountain, finally resting and falling asleep under the weeping willow tree, his old friend that greeted him year after year.

CHAPTER 2

Joe awakened before the other students, who would soon be rushing about to hear the various speakers. His eyes gazed upon the sunrise over the weeping willow tree. He decided to walk away from the summit to explore the surroundings, as the various pathways seemed to be calling out to him. The flowers popping out of the picturesque rocks lifted his spirits. He approached a forest of hundreds of uniquely shaped green trees. He rested and meditated upon the beauty surrounding him. A squeaky signpost caught his attention, as the high winds stirred: *The Village of Riches.* Curiously, Joe walked along the roadside through the jeweled entryway, viewing the homes and colorful gardens in the distance.

People were busily engaged in various activities throughout the village. It was a work day and traffic was heavy, as people rushed about. Some parents were driving their children to school, while others were dressed for the office. As Joe observed the communal scenes, he felt estranged from it all and began to wonder why he had no family to call his own. Everyone seemed so happy here in this village surrounded by beautiful homes and ranches. There were horses and dogs running about the hay-like grass behind the many white picket fences. Many homes had the names of the families posted upon the gates. Joe recognized one of the names on an old estate. It was an author he knew, a great teacher who had written many best-selling books. He had heard that over a hundred million copies had been sold worldwide. *Imagine that! So this is where he lives. Not bad.* As Joe glanced at the gardens surrounding the estate, he noticed a beautiful lady holding a newborn. Joe's thoughts began to reflect upon his own life. *Why did the person I loved so many years ago leave me? Why hasn't someone else come along to mend my broken heart?* Joe felt a sick feeling in his stomach as loneliness swept throughout his empty being.

Measureland

As Joe reminisced, he fell deeper into despair, realizing he had no home or family to call his own. He thought about his own books and wondered why they were not in the bookstores. Joe had never measured his success before by comparing it to others. Yet, as he walked along this village where everyone seemed to have a better life, all he could see was what he didn't have.

Joe meandered around for hours before he came to the Village Square, lined with unique designer shops. There was a winding river where he sat, reflecting upon his life. "Could this be my 'River of Sorrow'?" Joe asked himself. All he could see was that his life had passed him by, and there was so much more he wanted to experience. Emptiness swept through his body, his mind a mere depressed version of his tired spirit. "Why have I only managed to have a relationship with myself? Why do I find myself walking through the Village of Riches as a mere observer and not a resident? Am I not deserving to be here amongst the rich and successful?" Joe knew he had degrees of success, but all he could focus on now was the lack in his life.

Reflecting his own state of mind, everywhere Joe went he heard people comparing themselves to others. It seemed that people here measured everything. They counted their possessions. They lived with a scale that weighed their lives by accomplishments and material accumulations. It seemed to Joe that people had perfect little lives, all neat and tidy and in place, as they compared the talents of their children and rushed about to get the edge for their own families to fare well in the competitive world. Joe began to wonder for the first time in his life why he had only managed to create loneliness and struggle. "Is there some limiting force in the universe denying me my good? Do I have bad karma? Have I done wrong in a past life that I must pay the price now? Does the wind not blow riches in my direction or the rain only create storms without rainbows?

Why have I failed myself when I've tried so hard to succeed? Why is there no inheritance for me? My parents left not a penny to my estate! Bad luck or just a bad break?"

Joe was not looking at the half-full glass that he always talked about in his column. "The glass is always half empty and half full," he would preach. "When you see it as full, and are grateful for all that you do have, life is good." As Joe's consciousness had slipped into Measureland, he could not think about the blessings of his life. He certainly had good health and great genes inherited from his family, a far greater inheritance than paper riches. He had forgotten about his terrific intellect, not to mention his good nature and attractive sense of humor. He was a fine-looking man and came into this world with spiritual awareness. He knew so many people who suffered with ill health, weak genes and devastating poverty. All Joe could see in Measureland was his own lack.

Joe sat in the plush village tavern and drank a few jugs of imported beer, listening to the people talk about their houses, cars, clothing, bank accounts and vacations to exotic places. Everyone measured everything in relation to what others had and it was never enough for any of them. Competition was the name of the game: who looked younger for their age . . . whose children married

wealthy . . . graduated top of their classes of achievements . . . were admitted into the best schools for
their best chance to succeed as they grew older. They
discussed the importance of money and worshipped
those who had the most. They bragged about their possessions, including their own children in their tally of
goods. Some people changed their bodies to make themselves look not only more handsome, but younger and
more desirable in the marketplace, which is understand-
able. However, some went to extremes on an unattainable quest, having their fat sucked out of their bodies
and talked for hours about the latest plastic technology
for tucks and fad diets. Many people had synthetic sub-
stances injected into their faces to remove lines! Here in
Measureland, there was dissatisfaction in the air, and no
matter how much they had to enjoy, they were always
looking over their shoulders to see what they were miss-
ing. They wanted what everyone else had and looked to
others to see how they were faring. Egos were at their
finest tune, and the one thing that was certain here was
that no one ever had enough!

"I guess I've brought myself here by comparing
myself to others when I walked through the Land of
Riches. I've had so many chances in my life to have
saved and to accumulate money, set up a pension plan,

not to mention my sad credit score! Instead, I spent money as quickly as it came. I even gambled away so much of my money." He walked along and wondered why he was measuring his life in relation to other people's lives. "I have always delighted in the successes of others. How could I have become so bitter and resentful? I want everyone to have a good life. What has come of my thinking? I'm not really like these people in Measureland. It's never enough for them. 'What anyone else has, says, does or thinks has nothing to do with me! However, what I think will change my life forever.'" Those were the words in Joe's last column that he wrote. Now he was needing to remember his own teachings for himself.

"How do I get off this roller-coaster of comparisons?" Joe asked himself. "I never meant to feel jealousy. I wish every person in the world to have their best dreams come true. I was just lost in my own lonely life and wasn't guarding my mind and feelings of lack took over."

As he walked away, a bridge appeared upon the horizon. "Must be my 'Bridge of Struggle'," Joe thought. The more he tried to stop struggling within, the more discontent he felt in his life. "Why haven't I created the life I thought I would have?" He read the next signpost: VICTIMVILLE.

CHAPTER 4

The Town Hall was crowded with people rushing in to hear the new mayor.

"Poor people of Victimville," he shouted from the podium. "Don't blame yourself for your troubles. In Victimville, we are all just surviving our ill fates. We are a very poor town with little funds available. Many of you have been hit with life's tragedies and sadness beyond repair. Some of you have suffered great losses, while others have ill health or have experienced financial setbacks. Many people in our town are living in severe poverty. It's not your fault. Nothing is your fault. Never blame yourself. Financial disaster is commonplace here. It's a tough world, and you just never had a break. No one was there to lend you a helping hand when you needed one, and if they did, it was a mere pittance of what you needed.

"Some of you have lost your jobs and may have been downsized in the corporate world of greed. It's damn impossible to find another job. Why bother? We understand your dilemma. You can join the others who work for food. We take care of you in Victimville because we understand. No one escapes their ill fate. We are all doomed in this life, and it is certain to get worse. Count on it. Life brings one problem after another. Remember one thing: you can't help what has happened to you. You have bad karma. Maybe rotten people hurt you. I bet some of you were mistreated by your own families. Well, one thing is for certain: you didn't deserve all this suffering, did you?"

The crowds screamed with agreement, as the mayor continued his outpouring of martyrdom. "People of Victimville, I am here to deliver good news today. The great advantage of living here is that you are never alone! There will always be someone who will listen to your crying, and who will be understanding. Everyone here is in the same boat. Complain all you want. That's what we are good at doing in our little town of woes.

"Let's choose a partner to complain to and begin our annual contest to select the worst-off person in Victimville. If you are chosen, you'll win the grand prize of becoming my assistant."

Joe listened to one hard-luck story after another until his ears rang with discord. Everyone blamed someone else for his troubles. Some felt that they were doomed by life to live with an ill fate, and there was nothing they could do to change it.

Still, there were a few really terrible events that happened to people who were not in Victimville to blame life, but, rather, to learn how to forgive the wrongful deeds that had befallen them. Some were innocent victims of crimes, while others were wrongfully imprisoned. There were some who were abused and others born into the streets of poverty, alone and frightened without parents to guide and nurture them. Life had dealt blows to so many who longed for freedom and relief from their tortured existence. Joe felt saddened as he struck up a conversation with the lady seated next to him. "I want to find love and some day have a family and a home," she shared with Joe. "I don't blame anyone for the terrible tragedies that happened to me. I want to leave this town, but I can't seem to let go of the memories." Joe understood that life could be brutally hard for true victims. Yet, there were so many that were the blamers in life even when life had given them so much to be grateful for. The streets of Victimville were filled with people who seemed to enjoy complaining.

The votes were counted and the winner announced. The crowds were angry, as they screamed their objections. "Surely, she is not the worst off person in town." They were convinced that it was fixed, and it was just their rotten luck that they didn't win. "The whole contest is rigged," screamed the angry losers. The winner complained that she had won a thankless job without proper pay—a mere pittance of what she was worth. "Small wages for long hours of labor. How unlucky can a girl be?" With that, she rushed off with the mayor.

Joe's troubles seemed so small as he met the residents of the town. He walked to the nearest pub for a well-needed shot of rum, questioning himself as to how he arrived here amongst these suffering souls. "I sure thought I was an advanced thinker. This is not a place for miracle-minded people like me." He wondered what on earth went so wrong. He drank his rum and thought about how he had fallen into the trap of blaming life for his lack, feeling sorry for himself. There were so many hard-luck and unfair stories that he had heard. He wondered if it was their past life karma that brought these brutal events into this lifetime? He felt deep compassion for those who suffered through no doing of their own. There were many too sick to climb out of bed and others molested. He prayed for them all to find forgiveness and leave Victimville knowing that some were ready to get out and start a better life. He even prayed for the complainers who brought it all upon themselves. As he sent out great energy to everyone, he began his walk along the whining path out of Victimville, vowing never to be a blamer again . . . no matter what circumstances might come his way!

Still filled with great remorse for his life having passed so quickly and not turning out as he had hoped, he entered Regretland.

CHAPTER 5

Do you have regrets that haunt you, keeping you awake 'til all hours of the night? Do you regret missed opportunities, roads you might have traveled and places you wish you had visited? Have you lost your self-esteem and childhood passion, as disappointments washed them away? Has your need for security prevented you from taking chances that you wish you had taken? Have you withheld your love, keeping it buried within your heart, rather than giving it freely to another? So many people you wanted to love, while some you held onto for too long? Could you have earned more money, invested more wisely, saved for a day like today? Is your bank account depleted as you look back upon the steps not taken to grow wealth? Is this the stormy day you wish

you had saved for, as you count your pennies for your
daily bread? Are there homes you wish you had purchased or sold? Do you shed tears of sorrow for talents
left dormant for lack of use? Is your health failing for
lack of care of the only body you have been blessed with
. . . too much food and too little exercise? Has life passed
by while you were busy struggling to make it better?
Were there actions not taken that would have made
life richer but for the voice within that filled you with
doubts? Did you always make excuses, putting off new
beginnings for another day? Too busy planning ahead
to remember to laugh and play? Did you think there
would be a better time to be joyful, waiting for life to
improve? Could you have loved more and complained
less? Where is the "perfect person" you waited to find
that would be worthy of your love? Is it now too late to
share that love or has the moment passed into the dark
night, never to return? Too late to praise and honor
those who have made their grand appearance upon your
stage? Have they disappeared from sight? Did you take
abuse too lightly when you knew you deserved so much
more? Have you spent the greater part of your life focusing on your faults, rather than your value?

I am the Scroll Keeper and have come to inform you
that you have joined the millions of others who have

earned their way into Regretland. Some live here their entire lives, while others leave only to return time and again, escaping for brief periods. Few people ever leave without re-visiting.

You may have gotten out of Victimville, no longer being a blamer for your past, but still you bemoan your circumstances and, hereby, have arrived at the heavy gates of regret. Enter the land of regrets.

Joe tried to get out, but the iron gates closed behind him as he walked through a very dark passageway. Within seconds, he realized he was surrounded by tombstones in a large cemetery. There were messages carved upon each of the many stones. Three tombstones stood out as he read the words that would be impressed upon his mind forever: "COULDA ... WOULDA ... SHOULDA"

Suddenly an ominous black shadow stood next to Joe. A frightful laughter permeated the cold air throughout the cemetery. The Shadow spoke:

"Do you know why you have come to the cemetery of regrets?"

Joe tried to respond to the voice but was sharply denied the right to complete his sentence. "Well, I walked through the gates . . ."

"Silence, you fool of a human specimen. You'll

awaken the angry spirits who linger in their despair. You have given no thought to the wasteful life you live, or you would not be living in your past. You are here for the same reason they all arrive," roared the Shadow.

Joe inquired, "Who are you?"

Abruptly the Shadow shouted, "I am the Shadow of all regrets. Here lie the unfortunate ones who have been buried with all of their sorrow. They lived pitiful unfulfilled lives of discontent, but you are the fortunate one to still be alive with your regrets."

Joe was regretting this day as he stood before the ominous Shadow who reflected his state of mind. His eyes kept looking at the gate hoping to find a way to escape this horrific place.

"Some bury their regrets and escape," the Shadow continued, as if he could read Joe's intentions, "but even if they get out, they return again and again with their pathetic habits and excuses. You belong here. They all belong here. One day you will be buried here with the others, and you'll have many new friends with so much in common. You'll get exactly what you deserve . . . buried with your sadness and woes."

"No!" Joe screamed fearfully. "I'll find a way out of here. I don't belong here. I don't know what has happened to me lately, but I'll change."

The Shadow spoke in a somber tone. "You regret that there is no one to love. You have no family to call your own. Poor Joe, jilted by his lady with no one else worthy of your love, doomed to a lifetime of loneliness. You loved and lost and felt cheated by love, so you decided to cheat yourself and love no more. Rejected and filled with pain, you spend your days reminiscing. That's what they all do, always looking back at their mistakes. And of the billions of people on this planet, do you really believe there was not at least one other person you might have shared your life with, you selfish man? So many lonely people waiting for love to appear and you could find no one. Do you really believe that love would not have made its way to your doorstep had the door been open? Excuses, they all have excuses! You regret that life has passed so swiftly, leaving you unfulfilled and with less than you expected? You walked through the Land of Riches and saw not your own riches, but others with so much more than you? You wish to turn back life's clock, so you could dance to a richer tune, but you can't. It's too late. You've already gambled away your life, spending money and time on foolish games or trinkets to store in your closets. Where was the belief in yourself that you should have had? You expect others to believe in you when you do not think well of yourself? Where was all that faith hiding that you talked about to the masses in your column . . . the power of belief? You wish you had laughed and enjoyed your life, but now it's too late. There is no lighter tune to the music of your life. You are stuck with me where you belong."

Joe held his ears to stop listening but the Shadow would rule. "There is no escaping your miserable existence."

Joe firmly objected, "Stop. Enough." The Shadow continued, "You have lost your many chances to create your wealth, and even now, you choose to see only lack. You are here in Regretland—exactly where you belong."

"I'll find a way out!" cried Joe. "There must be a way out. It's never too late."

"Most people return so often that I become their best neighbor." The Shadow's laughter made every tombstone shake. "It's a rare specimen of a human who gets out of Regretland and never returns."

"How is it done?" Joe questioned in a begging manner. "How can one get out?" Joe ran to the gates. "I'm getting out of here, and I won't return!" A storm was brewing, dark clouds forming in the sky. Rain fell upon the ground.

As he faded into the mist, Shadow's voice quivered. "You regret too much to succeed. You'll never make it through Regret Therapy. That's where they all go to change their thought patterns. You'll be back. Most of them come back to me." His voice faded into the graves.

Joe was panicked as he pounded the gates that refused to give him freedom. He sat and stared at the stars in the black sky, longing to get out. He fell asleep hoping the morning would come quickly. As he opened his eyes to welcome the bright sun in an all-new day, a gatekeeper opened the locks and walked up a nearby hill. Joe yelled to him, "How do I find Regret Therapy?" The gatekeeper didn't answer, but his arm rose, and his finger pointed hesitatingly to the north where Joe spotted a town in the distance.

Joe rushed out of the cemetery and walked until his feet burned. Resting alongside a riverbank, he pondered what the Shadow had said. Staring into the face of the river, an older version of his former self, he began weeping. He cried for hours, longing for something he knew he could not have — his life back! The Shadow was right. He was young no longer, and it had all passed so quickly. "I really need therapy," he thought, as he rushed toward the next town.

CHAPTER 6

People were lined up for blocks registering for the fall semester. Everyone was assigned his own small room with one chair and a student's desk. They were told that they were to listen carefully for their own Guide, but no one was really certain as to what that meant. Then they were sent to the grand hall entitled

FAILURE HALL

Upon entering Failure Hall, everyone stopped to read the words that were written in bright gold letters:

NO MAN IS A FAILURE WHO
HAS FRIENDS

These words were quoted from the film *It's a Wonderful Life*.

26

Those famous words were followed with quotes from many who had entered the Hall at one point in their lives, only to leave a legacy of great success thereafter . . .

I have not failed. I've just found 10,000 ways that don't work. —THOMAS EDISON

Only those who dare to fail greatly can ever really achieve greatly. —ROBERT F. KENNEDY

We learn wisdom from failure much more than from success. We often discover what will do by finding out what will not do; and probably he who never made a mistake, never made a discovery. —SAMUEL SMILES

My great concern is not whether you have failed, but whether you are content with your failure. —ABRAHAM LINCOLN

Failure is simply the opportunity to begin again, this time more intelligently. —HENRY FORD

Every strike brings me closer to the next home run. —BABE RUTH

THE HEADMASTER

So, you have made your way through the doors of
Failure Hall. Congratulations and welcome to the greatest lesson of your life, for you are sitting in the very
same seats of the greatest minds of all time, the most
accomplished musicians, profound philosophers, brilliant scientists and Rhodes scholars. To name a few who
have felt the pains of rejection, the cries of poverty, or
the lowest ebb of self-esteem . . . There was Edison,
Ford, Einstein, and the Wright brothers . . . sat in the
seat you are warming today! Helen, without the ability
to hear words of inspiration, sat in defeat 'til the day she
decided to rise above her circumstances and find a better
way to live. There was Oprah, who became one of the
richest women in the world . . . and did she stop with
riches? No, for now she is a beacon of light and hope
to children of the world. They all have felt themselves
failures at one point in their lives . . . for the dictionary
defines failure as a cessation of proper performance as in
a *power failure*. The condition or fact of not achieving the
desired end or ends . . . is one who fails. Has your power
failed? Has your end come? Have you pronounced your
own demise? Are you powerless to continue? Do you
have a foot in the grave of tomorrow? Is your failure

a condition or have you deemed it a fact? Take notice:
Failure is a temporary condition and always brings us
closer to success, which is also temporary! All who sit in
these seats have learned Failure Hall's greatest lesson:
It's not over until the bell rings!

Dear students, your regrets are addictive habits
preventing you from moving forward to grander experiences. Change may not come easily, as misfortunes have
become a way of life. Childhood dreams are now but a
fantasy, and you awaken each day longing for the wonder and excitement you once felt as the sun rose with
all-new possibilities. Now you rise only to feel the dis-
appointment of your past that has ceased to exist along
with your hope and passion.

To restore your self-esteem and dignity and refill the
emptiness and disgrace you feel within your essence,
together we must move a mountain of despair and rebuild your hollow spirit with the memory hidden within
you of your true heritage. If you insist upon measuring
your misfortunes, then I instruct you to measure them
by comparing your life to those who have suffered more
than you. For should you have no family, though it be
lonely indeed, know that there have been others who
have been abused by theirs and wished they had none.
If you have no financial success to call your own, know

that there are millions with no food upon their tables. Perhaps it is best to not view your life by the troubles that have befallen you, but rather by the troubles that have escaped your door.

Surely today, you can reach within your heart and find something to be grateful for . . . for I assure you there are many who have not had a single day of sunshine. Your life is not about the experiences you've had, but rather, it is about the way you choose to look upon those experiences. For decades, this talk has changed millions of lives from tragedy to triumph by a mere changing of one's viewpoint. Where one person sees an end, another sees a new and grander beginning. There is a miracle at hand for he who decides to take a new vantage point in his life and see his past as a mere pebble on the sands of eternity. How you look upon yourself now will affect not only the rest of this lifetime, but the forever that awaits your creative genius.

In your designated *reflection* rooms, you will meet your special Guides, unique to each of you. They are physically invisible, but quite real as you are about to learn. They are waiting for you as they have patiently done for millenniums. You will hear them speak when you trust and open your ears to the voice within you. If you really want to leave Regretland, you'll pay attention to your Guide's every word as they explain the texts. Soon, you will realize that your Guides are quite familiar, as they represent your highest connection to the purest energy of the Universe. Be patient with your-selves in therapy as you uncover treasures long waiting to be revealed.

Joe sat in the tiny room, reflecting upon what the Headmaster had said, thus, wondering how he might view his life from a different vantage point. He felt some sort of energy in the room as he realized that he was not alone. He had been daydreaming about the repletion of happy times as this warm Presence seemed to demand Joe's attention. Joe looked over to the other chair and saw the Presence. He was a handsome and somewhat younger version of Joe, muscular and strong in appear-ance. Joe felt as though there were two of him, and the one he was looking at was the better of the two. He had heard many times that we have a *higher self*—one that is evolved and wise. It was as if he had another iden-tity, other than his own, that was now ready to reveal what Joe so desperately needed to know. Viewing this healthy and powerful specimen of himself, Joe spoke the first words. Their eyes met, but he uttered no words of welcome. Joe decided to accommodate the Presence

and, with a trembling voice, he asked, "Who are you?"
However, the Presence just peered into Joe's soul without uttering a single sound. Joe pleaded as he asked
again, "Are you really me? Are you my better self? Have
you come to help me to find myself or have you come
to taunt me while I'm in therapy?"

The Presence shook his head from side to side as if
saddened by Joe's lack of understanding. "I am not here
to demean you as I am that part of you that honors
you, even as we walk through storms together. I am
here to uplift you and introduce you to what is possible. Once, when you were born, I alone inhabited your
body. If only you knew that you were already perfect,
you never would have created a lesser self. Your judg-
ment of yourself has been your creation, for your past
is merely a set of changing conditions to which you
give meaning. You judge yourself harshly by focusing
on what you have or have not accomplished. I have
another scale by which I place an entirely different
value upon my work and productivity. Though I enjoy
and bestow upon myself the finest robes to wear and
castles to live within, I also value what a great lady who
sat at your desk many years ago had carved upon the
door as she went off into her world to assist the less fortunate:

At the end of life, we will not be judged by how
many diplomas we have received, how much
money we have made, how many great things we
have done . . .

We will be judged by . . . I was hungry and you
gave me to eat . . . I was naked and you clothed me
. . . I was homeless and you took me in . . .

—MOTHER TERESA

Another lady who sat in your chair reminded us:

When you leave this world, it matters not how
many people you know, but only how many
you love!   —ADRIENNE GOLDAY

Joe, you have arrived at a crossroad in your life. You
can continue to berate yourself for all the time you have
wasted procrastinating, the actions not taken, the talents
undiscovered, and the fortunes not made . . . or you can
look back upon all of it as the necessary seeds that made
it possible for you to succeed today to harvest your
crops. Which do you prefer? Haven't you spent enough
of your thinking upon that which no longer exists, other
than in the memory of a fool who longs for what he
may not retrieve? Let go of the fool who mourns his
life that has passed and see before your eyes the life that

waits. Look once more, dear friend, at all that no longer exists and give it new meaning that will serve you in living a better life today!

Text #1: Find Benefit In Everything That Has Occurred . . .

So, Joe healed old wounds, seeing them as stepping-stones for his growth. Where there had been lack, he saw degrees of abundance, and where there were mistakes, he deemed them lessons. At some point on his journey, he realized that he had done some extremely wonderful deeds and he began to credit himself for his caring nature and many friends. He began to understand how his entire life helped him to arrive at this amazing classroom where his *perfect self* was waiting to greet him and show him a better way to live.

Joe looked at his desk and contemplated

Text #2: Stop Competing With Yourself!

Joe's *perfect self* smiled with compassion as he explained, "When all that we do and all that we are and all we have is not enough, we compete with ourselves to always be more. We are in competition with ourselves when we feel that we can always be better than we are. When you honor yourself, reaching for the highest star, in an effort to be at your personal best, even when you don't reach the star, you have succeeded. Never judge yourself by the outcomes, but rather by the effort. This is a tough one, Joe, because we live in a world that sets us up with standards of superachievers, and we all measure ourselves by those setups. It's time to stop the comparisons and just do your best. When you have done your best, you will begin to appreciate your work and achievements and honor who you really are, not who you want to be. We are not our experiences, Joe. We are perfect energy forces having experiences. By not competing with ourselves to be other than what we are, we begin to love ourselves as we are. That means, Joe, that you are not a failure."

As Joe walked out of the classroom, he seemed to let go of more than his past judgments, for there was only one Joe that left the room, and you can be certain it wasn't the one he had created so many years ago that he now realized was his *lesser* self. He walked away with an all-new sense of self-esteem as he approached the steps leading back to Failure Hall.

THE HEADMASTER

Students, by now, many of you will understand what the English poet, John Keats, wrote so many years ago:

"Failure is, in a sense, the highway to success, inasmuch as every discovery of what is false leads us to seek earnestly after what is true and every fresh experience points out some form of error which we shall afterward carefully avoid."

So you see that it would be quite the feat to succeed without having failed or failed without having succeeded! So, then, let us take heed to what St. Jerome had to say: "Begin to be N O W what you will be hereafter." As you decide what to be now, remember to ask yourself: Would you rather have a lifetime of achievement or a calling that will bring you peace? I ask you also: If you had everything that you really have always wanted, what then? Do you really believe the things you have desired that have kept you from knowing a moment's peace would actually have brought you contentment? Surely, it has occurred to you that satisfaction is not found in the pleasures of a lavish lifestyle anymore than fame and recognition and riches bring fulfillment. Even those who create the most wonderful lives must one day face the changing of the experiential world. Let us reach to greater heights than we have ever imagined possible, where the treasures we amass are no more than a bonus as compared to the real fortunes discovered within ourselves. Know, then, that you are creating your world in a never-ending universe and shall have all that you dream of somewhere along the journey beyond your greatest expectations! You are not bound to only one lifetime. Celebrate the possibilities and create new scenes by knowing that they are only the beginning of a continual expression.

However, the good news of this never-ending expression comes with a bit of bad news today, I am sorry to say. For if you are gathered before us today, sadly, it means you have only one year to live in this particular lifetime. I hear your cries, but there is no time to waste. You must now decide what you shall do with this one year that is a great gift that you must cherish. This is your next assignment:

Text #3: Write Upon This Paper What Plans You Have Chosen For Your Last Year In This Lifetime.

Everyone was shocked but quickly adjusted, as no one wanted to waste any precious time. Joe decided that he would share as much of himself as possible with others, by contributing to their lives. He would buy his café with his meager savings and would laugh every day and love every day. Tears filled his eyes, as he realized the value of every second. Just when he designed a great and meaningful year, he, along with all the others, was informed that it was only an exercise and not their final year. The purpose, they were told, was to make it easier to complete the next and last part of the program, wherein they would bury their regrets.

"Students, there are buses waiting for you that will take you back to Regret Cemetery, where you will complete the course with the final text."

Text #4: Write Every Regret You Have Upon Paper And Throw
Them Into The Fire . . . Turning Regrets Into Ashes,
Then To Be Buried Into The Ground Forever . . .

REGRET #1 _____

REGRET #2 _____

REGRET #3 _____

REGRET #4 _____

They were informed that the semester was completed. Some of the students stayed in Regretland and chose not to leave, but most couldn't get out fast enough and were determined never to return. Upon leaving, there was a ritual to follow in order to gain access out of the gates. Everyone had to sign their name upon the famous

WALL OF AGREEMENT

Whereupon they made a promise to themselves:

Wall of Agreement
I, _____, promise to live life without regrets!

Joe burned and buried every one of his past regrets and then signed his name upon the wall. He, like everyone else who made the promise, was given a T-shirt that read

GRADUATE OF REGRET THERAPY

There was no celebration, as most students rushed out of the cemetery as fast as their legs could run. As the iron gates closed behind Joe, he vowed never to look back again. He walked into the dark night with an excitement that had long been dormant as he began to think about what he could create for his future. He smiled at the very thought!

Soon, he approached a bright yellow signpost as the next town awaited him with open arms!

CHAPTER 7

Joe saw the signpost ahead of him and decided not
to visit, for he knew that it's not wise to wait for the
future to find your happiness. It's great to make plans
and have goals, but Joe knew far too many people who
put off living, thinking only of what tomorrow would
bring. Future living brings fear and worry. However,

as he walked away, he was tempted, as he wondered
if he would really be able to have the lifestyle that he
desired. Joe's thoughts went to the future and immedi-
ately he started to worry about his health, wondering if
it would hold up, and how long might he live. Joe kept
walking, and just as he no longer regrets anything in his
past, he is cautious not to jump too far ahead. Instead,
he decided to remain on the path the entire way back to
Pinnacle Mountain to where he had begun this insight-
ful journey.

As he walked taller and felt stronger, Joe smiled to
himself, knowing he was in a good place. He had a feeling of harmony within himself and a newfound self-con-
fidence as he looked around at the beautiful trees and
glorious day that seemed to be waiting for his notice.

Return to *Pinnacle Mountain*

CHAPTER 8

Back at the retreat, Joe sat at the fireside, excitedly waiting to join his peers as they viewed the schedule of speakers for the next day at Pinnacle Mountain. As they were on the same mission, they felt a kinship with one another. They returned each year hoping that this would be the pinnacle of self-discovery that would finally be uncovered. Perhaps that is why they named this place *Pinnacle Mountain.*

In the morning, the crowds of students entered the various lecture halls. Joe, feeling quite liberated and confident, decided to listen to Master Key, whose name denoted special significance, as rumor would have it, because it is said that he held the *key* to the highest and most precious place in human consciousness. Master Key was also famous for the kaleidoscopes that he made, which he explained serve as a reminder to him that all energy is constantly changing and how nothing that is physical ever stays the same. He enjoyed a reputation for always being late to his own classes, as he refused to wear a timepiece or live by clock time. His topic would be "Living In A Timeless Universe."

"Students and future Avatars, I humbly address you today as I know I stand before giants in the making! Though you may not yet have recognized your role in the drama of humanity, I am well aware that each one of you shapes the world with every thought conjured up by your beautiful minds! Potent beyond your wildest imagination are those thoughts that you ponder all day long! Beware and stand guard at that gate, as you have the potential to shape the destiny of millions.

"Do not take these words lightly, for today I am here to help you change the fortunes of your life with the power that lives within you. Your life may be reshaped to your liking by taking control of your world by this understanding. Do you have a desire to change your life and the world as it appears before you? Without changing anything but your thoughts, you shall begin to change the world. You are the energy that creates new forms. We live on planet earth, and how we each think about the earth will change the earth. When you give thought to the Earth's waters and care about its purity, you will be a part of the force that creates steps toward that purification . . . and when you give thought to the atmosphere surrounding the beautiful planet that allows us to live this life, you will be creating new and better technology that will sanctify the air. Your power to change circumstances is far greater than you know. It is always one person whose passion is felt by hundreds of others that creates new positions and events that begets hundreds more and then thousands to take action and change a thing for the better . . . or worse. The unfolding universe awaits us with lavish abundance, stored treasures, waiting for you to dare to indulge and accept. Instead, you refuse to take charge of this power that has been bestowed upon you, and you ask for your good as if you were a beggar. I am here to inform you that you are not a beggar, but a King with whom to be reckoned. Firstly, you must accept your position and know that you are the form-makers of your worlds. We live in a world of form, not time. Material forms keep changing, giving the appearance of time. Celebrate the changing scenes before you and examine your beliefs! Let's create the unfolding universe before us with more laughter and love, with joy and compassion for one another. Just as we view the changing colors and shapes of a kaleidoscope, so do our lives change with every passing thought and idea we embrace!

"We are always living in what I have named the WORLD OF IS . . . *I-nfinite S-pirit*. Everything changes and IS always new as the cells in your body renew themselves daily. There IS no time . . . energy simply IS changing, thus, giving the appearance of a past, present, and future. All that was and all that will be exists in the grand, ever-changing forms in the world of infinite spirit!

"Let us each design new events to appear before our eyes and become Makers of Dreams, for you are the energy that creates dreams. Create joy where there has been sorrow; love where there has been hatred; and peace where only war has existed on our beautiful planet Earth."

Joe was in awe of the concept of a timeless universe and changing forms in the ever-moving flow of life. As fate would have it, Master Key was right alongside him as the class ended. They walked together for many hours amongst the tall forest around Pinnacle Mountain. They lost track of *clock time*, as Master Key only noticed the changes in the landscape, as the sun rose and the moon shaped the nights. Key invited Joe to be his guest. They arrived at the tiny village where Key's ancestors had lived before him for many generations, and he had lived most of his life.

Joe and Key became great soul friends, enjoying each other's company as they had much in common. Key was, however, extremely light-hearted, yet Joe was much more serious natured. Laughing easily and always seeing the good in everything, Key was the most joyful person that Joe had ever encountered. They both enjoyed talking about the laws of physics, and eventually Joe began to see the world around him more intrinsically. As they appreciated the beauty of nature unfolding, it truly was a world without time. They fished at a picturesque lake near Key's cottage and had no thoughts of what life was before or what was to be. There was only that which was unfolding before them that made up their days.

Joe became an apprentice in the designing of the kaleidoscopes, and he enjoyed the magnificent colors and ever-changing shapes as they continually moved.

Key understood that his friend was struggling with the inevitability of loss, aging, sickness and death, and that no matter how great a *thinker* he had become, it simply would not let him go. Key's ancestors had spoken of a prince named Siddhartha Gautama, who lived in North India over 2500 *human measured* years ago, who dedicated his life to discovering a solution for this problem of human suffering. He became known as the Buddha, the Blessed One, and the Happy One, whose enlightened findings illuminated the lives of countless millions who followed in his footsteps. Buddha found peace in the world, and these teachings Key shared with Joe.

> *Everything arises and passes away.*
> *When you see this, you are above sorrow.*
> *This is the shining way.*
>
> *Existence is sorrow.*
> *Understand, and go beyond sorrow.*
> *This is the way of brightness.*
>
> *Existence is illusion.*
> *Understand, go beyond.*
> *This is the way of clarity.*

Joe wasn't relieved by these words, as he had hoped for something more tangible that would bring some joy into his reality. He understood that he had to get over his sorrow and accept what is in the grand World of 1s.

If it was enough for Siddhartha to discover beauty in all things, then he decided he had best capitulate and get busy with the business of living, and that is, after all, the business everyone is in. Joe examined his beliefs, realizing their role in creating his life. Every day he reconditioned his thinking. He learned how to create his world by taking new actions. He designed the forms before they actually appeared through visualization. He moved his body often in order to keep it agile and younger. When he felt the aches and pains of aging, he visualized pure energy flowing into his form, and he drank fresh water from pure springs and ate organic greens, while healing reshaped his body and revitalized his cells. He accepted only thoughts of a perfect vessel that must be cared for and honored, and soon, his body responded, though it was no easy feat. Over and over, Key would remind him that Infinite Spirit is the energy force that creates all the bodies in the world. We make everything change because everything always has to change in the wonderful world of forms, physical matter. As Buddha promised, his suffering diminished as he stopped trying to change that which could not be changed. He stopped fighting with his sorrow over aging and, instead, focused on what he could improve that was within his power, and that made all the difference in his life.

Everyone in the village was proud of Key's kaleidoscopes that were purchased around the globe. One day
as Joe squinted, peering into one of the jeweled scopes,
he intuitively knew that he must leave the familiar com-
fort of Key's world, return to the Village of Riches, and
recreate his own. Only this time he would rebuild his
life without measurements or comparisons. He would
be the best he knew how to be, without the weights and
burdens of what he had deemed to be past failures. He
was free to set his own standards of accomplishment.
Joe looked for the benefit in all things past and present
as he entered Successland.

CHAPTER 9

For many years, Joe had learned the so-called *laws of success*. He guarded his thoughts, wrote down his goals, planted many seeds, and experienced many actual successes in his life. Yet it is only in the constant taking of new actions that success becomes a continual part of our lives, because success, as Joe was reminded by the Headmaster of Failure Hall, is just as temporary a condition as failure.

Joe humbly entered the Land of Riches, no longer as an observer, but as a resident, feeling life's pulse within his heart and an appreciation of each breath with an all-new awareness!

He rented a small room behind one of the large estates from a wonderful family, and they soon became friends. He assisted them in designing their gardens, and since he often dined with them, he baked a variety of breads as his contribution. There was a tiny café that he frequented; he befriended the proprietor. He accepted an offer to be the new baker in the café that was located in the center of the town square. It wasn't much of a place, but Joe treated it as though it were the grandest designer café in Paris. He kept it immaculately clean and he took pride in his creations. The word spread rapidly that there was a great baker who made the world's best buns. Soon, the owner offered Joe a small percentage of his profits as he felt they were a direct result of Joe's talents and reputation. This allowed Joe to increase his savings. One day the owner informed him that he had to sell his café so he could move to his sister's village since she was ill. He informed Joe that he couldn't possibly sell it to anyone else, given that Joe had caused it to become a successful enterprise. Though Joe's meager savings were not nearly enough to match the selling price, he now understood that his own belief would create his reality. He made an offer to the proprietor to purchase the café for half the asking price, not because it was worth half, but that was all that he had saved. "To make up for the other half, I will share the profits with you and you will always have some income for the rest of your life!" They agreed on a percentage of profits. Joe was now the proud owner of the café. He painted a sign with the new name in large letters: *Moneybuns Dream Café*. Known for the best buns around, it was the special talks that Joe gave at the noon hour each day on creating money that made it questionable whether people were frequenting the café for the buns or the inspiration. They loved listening to Joe's stories about the different mental lands he had traveled to in his discovery of truth. They left the café feeling richer in body and spirit.

One noontime talk went something like this:

"I once visited this rich and beautiful village where we now live, but I felt poor because I was comparing my riches to others. I focused on what I wanted my life to be and felt that I had failed. I had no money in the bank or a home of my own. As a lonely and poor man, I became embittered and saddened. Since then, there have been a number of lessons that I've embraced. The first, and most significant, was the realization that my scales of measuring success were in great need of a transformation! I left this village as a failure and returned to you as a Maker of Dreams. I am making my own dreams come true as we speak. I have always dreamt of sharing recipes of wisdom and sweets with friends who would gather at my café. This long-desired vision has come to fruition, as my belief in myself has changed. I no longer measure my success in life by the scales of what I have or have not achieved, nor do I compare my life to another's. I have learned that success is an ongoing dream that never ends, and that we shall each behold fortunes beyond our wildest expectations! If you feel discouraged and worn, know that you hold the power to change your life, as life is continual change."

The walls of the Moneybuns Dream Café held a library of success, which contained some of the greatest books ever written by the most influential writers of the ages. Joe often quoted from these wisdom books. He shared that as important as the books are, there comes a point in our lives when we must stop studying and start living! "Revisit your library of success and be motivated and inspired, yet do not wait another day to take the actions necessary to create new dreams on your list. There comes a point in everyone's journey when he realizes he has waited far too long to get into the motion of his life. There are too many lectures on *how to achieve*, yet too few steps taken in the process of achievement."

They came from every village and town to hear Joe speak. Soon he opened more cafés in neighboring towns. In time, he moved out of his tiny room behind the estate and purchased a home of his own. Joe filled every room with *Hand of God* books to inspire his friends when they visited. Laid upon the coffee table was his own book about getting out of Regretland. He taught people to find the benefit in everything that ever happened to them and, in so doing, they would free themselves of regret thinking. People wrote letters to Joe from all over the globe, sharing their personal stories of how their lives were transformed when they stopped regret thinking. This was only the beginning of Joe's journey, as he grew in his soul and became quite the teacher in his own right!

Joe was quoting from Dr. Ernest Holmes, one of the greatest truths he had ever heard, "The storehouse of nature is filled with infinite good awaiting the touch of our awakened thought to spring forth into manifestation in our lives!" One of the patrons put his coffee down upon the table and interrupted the talk. "Where is this storehouse of good in my life? I lost my job, my family left me, and I've been too sick to work. How should I *awaken* my thoughts? Can you tell me that, as you stand up and make it sound so easy? What would you know of troubles?" Joe continued to read from Dr. Holmes' book, as he knew the answer was there. "We could accomplish whatever it is possible for us to conceive. Life externalizes at the level of thought. Daily we must control all thought that denies the real, affirm the Divine presence within us; then as the mist disappears before the sun, so shall adversity melt before the shining radiance of our exalted thought!"

Joe smiled warmly at the man, and helped him through his regrets. He showed them all how to see life as constantly changing energy, and he helped them to bring newness into their lives while appreciating the beauty unfolding before them. "Always take new actions in the direction of your dreams, no matter how small! This is how we recreate our circumstances in the World of IS." So many people changed their beliefs in themselves and became Makers of Dreams! They came to realize that all that IS happening IS the infinite spirit of energy changing its form in the physical world, and that our beliefs constantly change within the World of IS.

Joe made friends in every town, and his life was no longer lonely. One day, he befriended a lady who asked to understand more about the *timeless universe*. She said that she understood that time was nonexistent as forms constantly change, thus giving the illusion of time passing. Joe couldn't believe how beautiful she was. They shared philosophy and time stopped.

Eventually, she became his wife, so that they would have unlimited *time* in the *timeless universe* to make new creations together. That's how Joe found love—just like that!

One day, that man who had no job phoned Joe and asked to work at one of the cafés. "I'll work for free to prove myself, if necessary," he told Joe. "I am recreating myself. I understood what you said. We are spiritual energy creating matter. Our bodies are the physical manifestations created by our energy. We create the world of form-reality. What we believe about our world of forms, also called matter, actually shall affect it accordingly. Change what you believe, and you change your world. I believe that I have found a home right here in the café, Joe." With that, he was given the job. The two of them were always available to explain to anyone willing to listen how they could begin a new life.

However, there were many people who listened to them trying to change their thinking, and repeatedly slipped into their old thought patterns of doubt and disbelief. They remained victims of their circumstances because they really believed that there was no chance for life to improve. With great compassion, Joe understood how difficult it is for one confined in a chair to believe that there is a chance to improve his life . . .

or for someone who mourns for his beloved to love another. He knew, however, the limitless power that we have to reshape and recreate new circumstances. He knew that our energy is not confined to our bodies, and that with our minds we are able to begin to create new worlds for ourselves. When our physical bodies cease to exist, our energy lives for eternity! In this, Joe found peace, though many eyebrows in the café were raised as he shared how love reappears as the great imposter. "Those we love will always reunite with us though we may not always recognize them. Love always multiplies when given away—defying the laws of physics."

Joe talked to everyone about their amazing power to create their dreams in the factory of their minds. He was a great teacher on the subject of creating money. By giving great sums of money to yourself in your mind as a gift, you prepare yourself for its arrival. The more actions you take to create channels for its arrival, the more money will flow. He was an advocate of creating pictures of how he wanted his life to be, as it formed before him! "Never focus on all that you don't want to have happen, because you will get more of what you don't want!" Joe reminded the coffee drinkers, as they reshaped their lives right there at the café, writing their dreams upon their napkins! "Instead, give yourself many gifts and focus upon that which will soon take form. This is how we change our lives, one gift at a time! What happens is astounding! The world around you will accommodate you as opportunities and people will appear who can pave the path for gifts to arrive in physical form." Joe explained how once we accept the gifts mentally, our belief system actually begins to expect the arrival of the gifts that we gave ourselves. When our beliefs change, everything changes. Joe explained, "So instead of viewing your life, for instance, without the relationship you long to have, gift it to yourself and prepare for the arrival of this person in the physical realm." The customers became quite the *gift givers* and word spread about this technique that allows us to accept greater love and wealth. The crowds continued to grow at the cafés and Joe became a very busy man.

Even though Joe now had a successful lifestyle and someone to share it with, along with many friends, he knew that something within him remained unfulfilled. He had improved his lifestyle dramatically and loved his work, but he still felt a sadness within his soul as he lay awake at night wondering why all this success had not brought the bliss that he had searched for his entire life? "Perhaps this thing called *bliss* does not exist in the human drama," Joe convinced himself as he decided to quiet his mind, stop thinking, and enjoy the *good life* he had finally created.

One day as Joe delivered a talk on how everything constantly is in a state of flux, it occurred to him that everything he cherished would one day vanish. He understood that he could not hold on to his wealth, his money, his lifestyle, his loved ones, or even his own body, for that matter. He would lose everything in the physical world of form and there was absolutely nothing he or anyone else could do to change the fact that everything changes. "I suppose this is why the Buddha said that *life is sorrow; go beyond it*, but how do we go beyond it?" Joe was now determined to discover how to not only go beyond his sorrow, but also, at long last to know what it is to have *bliss*. He appreciated his life now, but it was not enough to satisfy him, and even though he had gone from failure to success, he had to reach for more.

He knew that his friend, Key, was thought to possess the key to uncovering the highest level of human consciousness. He decided to visit him and take a long-needed vacation. After packing his bag, he arranged with his employees some time off and set out on his journey of discovery once again, only this time with aspirations of reaching the blissful summit of his existence. He wondered if it were really a possibility or was he just a foolish old man in search of an unattainable goal? All he knew was that he had to try!

Master Key lived in a tiny village often referred to as Kaleidoscope Village. The village folks enjoyed the colorful gems of the various scopes, and it helped them to relax and reminded them how beautiful life can be! This is where Joe had learned about the changing forms and the World of IS, and now, he was returning in search of yet another treasure.

There was a key in the door to Key's cottage as if company were expected. Joe hesitantly turned the key and called out for his friend, who wasn't home. He decided to sit and wait for Key's hopeful return. Glancing around the enchanting room, he noticed the uniquely shaped kaleidoscopes, some quite large and others small but each beautifully decorated. The room was cozy and warm, and Joe closed his eyes and rested, feeling a sense of security in Key's surroundings.

He awoke and walked to the kitchen table where a large paper caught his attention. It was a letter with Joe's name written in extremely large letters, so that he would discover it. With utter amazement that a letter had been left for him, he sat down and eagerly began to read.

To my dear friend, Joe,

I expected that one day you would return in your quest for truth and bliss, as all of life's many successes hold not an ounce of such splendor!

By now, you have a wonderful life, filled with love and wealth beyond your earlier dreams. It is no surprise to me that you have achieved such abundance, as you were an earnest student of the laws of creative energy. You have made your many dreams come true!

Now you seek the wisdom of the most evolved sages who have walked the earth . . . but I must prepare you that this wisdom comes with a price! Your focus in life shall change and you will see the world in a new way. Though it be a "better way to live," there are many who will misunderstand you, for they live in a different land. You have turned the key to unlocking this wisdom when you were no longer satisfied with mere success in the physical realm. As you enter the Land of Deity, your rewards will be far greater than any you have ever known. You will be a rarity amongst the masses and your kingdom shall be infinite and grand! What will appear that you have given up, the

world as you have known it, shall be replaced with
a world of indescribable bliss! Every sage, teacher,
and avatar of all worlds who has embraced this
"message" live in eternal harmony . . .

Behold the sacred papers with the message of
my ancestors stored within the giant kaleidoscope
. . . and enter . . . the land of deity!

Key

Joe was in a state of awe. He noticed that there
was yet another page of Key's letter that he had
missed.

P.S. Joe, I am traveling in a distant land . . . we
shall meet again in one of the many worlds before
us . . . Until then, think of me every now and then,
for I will always be as close as your thoughts! Take
good care of the kaleidoscopes as my gift to you.
Share them with others . . . Enjoy the beauty as it
unfolds.

Joe looked inside the giant tube anxiously awaiting his fortune!

Land of Deity

Land of Deity Land of Deity Land of Deity

CHAPTER 10

THE MESSAGE

You are a dream maker
And you are the dream
Of the maker of all dreams . . .
That you shall create the one dream . . .
That every maker of dreams reaches
Supreme love . . . fulfilling his destiny!

You can't love yourself until you love
Everyone . . . you can't love everyone until
You love yourself . . . Everyone is One!

63

Tears filled Joe's eyes, as he understood that the "One Dream" meant there is no "everyone." There is only "one." Written upon the antique kaleidoscope was a quotation from Gandhi: "When one person reaches Supreme Love, it is sufficient to nullify the hatred of millions."

The common denominator that connects us to one another is love, and it multiplies as it is given away. The more we give of our love, the more we have of it to give. Even when our physical form disappears, love remains and reappears as the great imposter, always eternally reuniting us to those we have loved. Though not always recognizable, we meet over and over in worlds to come. All this, Joe suddenly knew to be truth. He realized that in loving others, we love ourselves, and thus, reach Supreme Love, fulfilling our own true destiny!

In all of Joe's days to follow, he enjoyed his life in a completely new way, seeing himself in others. He looked within himself and discovered a whole world of new emotions. Other people's dreams became more important than his own and when great things happened to them, he celebrated because he knew it was happening to a part of himself! He felt great compassion for those who had not yet received "The Message," and he found it easier to forgive their actions. Though he could not be in the company of all people who had yet to learn great life lessons before they would stop their destruction, he would send them his loving energy with his heart, seeing them as evolving souls in the making! He understood that there is only ONE energy that we are . . . in many, many physical forms. Every One is One and One is Every One! This is how Joe, an ordinary kind of guy, fulfilled his destiny and became extraordinarily blissful as he saved his world.

Reader,

We invite you to share your stories with us for future "Regretland" books! Tell us how you have personalized "Joe" through your own experiences of all of life's mental lands! How has getting out of Regretland changed your life? Or are you stuck in Measureland? Do you bounce back and forth or have you mastered your thinking?

Want to share your regrets? Successes? Which land are you currently visiting? Are you between Successland and the Land of Deity?

Have you looked at a kaleidoscope lately? Are you finding the benefit in everything, past and present? We want to know the "Joe" who lives in you!

Send your Regretland stories to us at

regretlandbooks@gmail.com

Book Orders: (818) 451-8828
www.regretlandbooks.com

Regretland Books
1014 S. Westlake Blvd., Suite 14-195
Westlake Village, California 91361

Call to schedule lectures and book signings
with Adrienne Golday!

We look forward to hearing your personal success stories.

Dear Adrienne Golday,

When I began reading your story of Joe, I intended to read just a few pages then come back to it later. I had other pressing matters on my mind. I was wrong, I could not stop. It was so captivating, I felt as if I was reading my very own story.

Joe's story is short, simple, but profoundly relevant. Its ten chapters are like a ladder with ten links, each leading the reader higher and higher in his/her quest for that ultimate state of true success, joy and bliss.

Ever since my early years, I have been an avid reader of self-help books. I credit much of my academic and economic success to the inspiration these books have given me. I can sincerely say, however, that the story of Joe supersedes anything

I have ever read. It is an inspired story. It is destined to be a classic that withstands the test of time, a blueprint for life, a guide to the young and old for a successful, fulfilling and joyful life.

Adrienne, you have distilled the wisdom of the ages into a short story form. Your book will be a priceless gift that I am anxiously waiting to share with all my friends. It will give all of us hope and courage to keep on living and, most of all, it propels us to that level beyond measured success, the level of abiding inner contentment, peace and bliss.

Thank you for allowing me the privilege of being one of your first readers.

—JABBOUR S. SEMANN,
DH.SC., MS, MPH, PT

My wife and I love Adrienne's new book. She boils down the world's most enlightening treatises from Aristotle to Freud into sage nuggets. On a daily basis, I am liberated from negative moods by remembering these gems. If I start feeling sorry for myself, I think of her chapter on Victimville, which uplifts me to a good place. Britannica's Great Books purports to contain the wisdom of the ages in 54 volumes. Adrienne has distilled that wisdom into one small book. Her brilliant insights have truly enriched my life.

—JOE SORRENTINO Attorney/judge,
and author of the best-selling novel
Up from Never

Upon reading Regretland *by A. Golday, I wanted to give a copy to everyone I know. It is the most informative and entertaining concept on how we approach life and the way in which we can stay centered and balanced. I read from cover to cover non-stop, one great chapter after another, and was enlightened and inspired! Thousands of self-help books have made their way into my life of meta-physical studies and teaching, but* Regretland *has made its way into my heart and spirit.*

—FREDA AMSEL Numerologist, writer,
lecturer/teacher

"It's impossible to be grateful and regretful at the same time."

"Time can't be measured in a timeless universe."

"When living in 'Deity Land,' contact everyone you've ever known to say hello, and you'll never be lonely again. This is life's Rolodex for Deities."

All of the coffee drinkers wear their "Regretland" T-shirts with pride:

"I made it out of Victimville"

"Lost in Measureland"

"Graduate of Failure Hall"